# Tweenie clock

This Annual belongs to...

Asèie

First published in 2001 by BBC Worldwide Ltd, Woodlands, 80 Wood Lane, London, W12 OTT.
Text, design and illustrations © 2001 BBC Worldwide Ltd.
Based on the Tweenies television programme produced by Tell-Tale Productions Ltd for BBC TV.
'BBC' and 'Tweenies' are trademarks of the British Broadcasting Corporation and are used under licence.
Tweenies © BBC 1998. © BBC Worldwide Ltd. 2001. Licensed by BBC Worldwide Ltd. ISBN 0-563-476419.
Written and edited by Andrea Wickstead and Sarah O'Neill.
Designed by Susan Jackman. Makes by Susan Jackman.
Colour origination by Polestar Digital Watford Ltd, Watford.
Printed and bound by Proost Nv. Turnhout, Belgium.
Photography by Christopher Baines, Alan Olley and Bruce Coleman Ltd. Illustrated by Bill Titcombe, Andy Holt,
Alan Craddock, Sonia Canals, Jenny Tulip, Alison Carney, Lorna Kent, Ian Cunliffe, Lisa Smith, Beccy Blake and
Emma Holt. Thanks to Stefano, Chiara, Layth, Luke, Sumiyya, Aleena and Rebecca who appear in this book.

# where will it stop?

# Dinosaur dreams

"STOMPEROONY!" shouted Milo, as he stomped about like an elephant – STOMP, STOMP – but he stomped right into Fizz.

"Oh, Milo, that was really annoying," said Fizz. She decided to keep out of Milo's way and shut herself in the playhouse to talk to her best friend, Susan.

Now, Susan wasn't a person, she was a small, stripy dinosaur, but she was a very good listener.

"Did you see what Milo did, Susan?" asked Fizz, as Susan appeared in front of her like magic. "Can I sit with you until I feel better?" Susan smiled and nodded.

Milo, Bella and Jake peered through the playhouse window to check on Fizz.

"I think I've upset Fizz," said Milo. "Oh look, she's talking to herself now!" They all looked at Fizz chatting away, but they couldn't see anyone else!

Milo knocked and they went inside.

"Are you alright, Fizz?" asked Bella.

"Yes, I'm just talking to my bestest friend, Susan," replied Fizz, "she's very good at listening."

4

"There's nothing there, except fresh air," said Milo, scratching his head.

"You've got to look VERY closely," said Fizz. So they looked very hard indeed and suddenly... Susan appeared like magic.

"WOW! A DINOSAUR!" gasped Bella, Milo and Jake.

"She's lovely," sighed Bella, admiring her pretty blue stripes.

"She's not a real dinosaur though, Fizz," said Milo. "Real dinosaurs are big and brown and green and they STOMP around."

"Dinosaurs can be any 'saurs' in dinosaur dreams," sniffed Fizz. "I dream about dinosaurs a lot – I like their names, like Diplodocus and Apatosaurus and Stegosaurus.

After I've dreamt about real dinosaurs, I start to make up my own."

"Really, Fizz? Dinosaur dreams? I'd like to be in one of those," cried Jake.

"Well, let's all dream, then," said Fizz. So they closed their eyes. When they opened them, they were surrounded by dinosaurs!

"Look at all these dinosaurs!" gasped Milo. "JURASSEROONY!"

"Wow-wee!" said Jake, as he looked through the gigantic leaves at the creatures that wandered past them.

"Are these Specialsaurs, Fizz?" he asked.

"They can be any 'saur' you imagine them to be," replied Fizz.

So they all dreamed up dinosaurs...

Psychadellosaurs were rainbow coloured while Silversaurs gleamed. There were Spottysaurs and Stripysaurs and Squareosaurs and Circlesaurs. They spotted Jellysaurs and Wobbletops and Cuddlesaurs too, while Kiteosaurs floated by high in the sky.

They floated through their dinosaur dreams and made lots of dinosaur friends – big ones, small ones, round ones, square ones. Which dinosaurs will you have in your dinosaur dreams?

Based on the story written by Will Brenton.

# Messy Time Eggboxosaurus

To make your very own Eggboxosaurus (an eggstremely rare dinosaur that lived many years ago in the eggrassic era), you will need:

two egg boxes  tissue paper  paints glue

stomperoony!

**1** First, paint the egg box green, with yellow spots.

**2** Cut out four egg holders from the other egg box and paint them red with green toe nails! Stick them to the bottom of the other egg box.

glue

**3** Draw a face on another egg holder and stick it to the egg box using a thick rolled up piece of tissue paper.

**4** Do the same for the tail, but stick a big ball of tissue paper at the end to make a fierce club tail!

**5** Finish your Eggboxosaurus with twisted tissue paper spikes!

Bring these dinosaurs to life using your coloured pencils –
if you dare! Don't forget to join the dots first.

11

# The day I met

The day I met the dinosaurs,
It came as quite a shock.
They stood next to our washing line,
Chewing Mummy's frock.

I met a Diplodocus –
She'd quite an appetite.
She ate our neighbour's garden,
In one humungous bite!

I stared at a Triceratops,
Who poked me with his horn.
Then blew me right across the yard,
With one enormous yawn.

# the dinosaurs!

Rex smiled at me and told me that
He'd take me home for tea.
I thought he meant I'd eat with him...
...not that the tea was me!

He picked me up and stomped about,
Then tossed me in the air.
He caught me in his massive mouth,
And left me sitting there!

I realised I could get away,
When out popped his big tongue.
I used it as a diving board –
One bounce and off I sprung!

I told my mum and she just laughed,
But YOU know that it's true.
I met the dinosaurs one day –
You might just meet them too!

# Marching band

"Left, right, left, right!" ordered Bella, as the others marched along behind her. They all had their instruments – Milo banged his big drum, Fizz crashed the cymbals together and Jake tooted on his trumpet. Bella was the band leader, so she twirled her wand at the front.

"About turn!" she cried. That meant stop and turn around, but the others didn't realise that and when she stopped, they all crashed into her.

Milo landed on Jake's trumpet and squashed it.

"Poor Jake, he loved that trumpet," sighed Fizz. Jake was very upset. "Milo broke my trumpet," he told Doodles, sobbing. Doodles offered him his bone, but as Jake pointed out, you can't play music on a bone.

Milo felt really guilty, but then he had an idea. They all got busy in the messy time area.

"We've got to make lots of small instruments," he told the others.

They made a trumpet from paper, a big bass drum from a hat box and cymbals from saucepans.

"What are we making these for?" asked Bella and Fizz. "It's a surprise!" smiled Milo.

When they had finished making the instruments, they all gathered at the surprise stage.

When the curtains opened...
It was Jake the one-man band! He had cymbals tied to his legs – CLANG! A cardboard trumpet – TOOT! TOOT! And a big box drum – TUM-TE-TUM!

"Instead of just playing the trumpet, I thought Jake could play *all* the instruments!" laughed Milo.

TOOT TOOT!

TUM-TE-TUM!

TUM-TE-TUM!

CRASH CLANG!

CRASH CLANG!

Based on the story written by Alan Mcdonald.

# Puzzle it out!

Follow the lines to match the Tweenies to their instruments!

Some instruments make a noise with their strings, some make a noise when you blow them and others need to be hit.
Can you decide which ones are which?

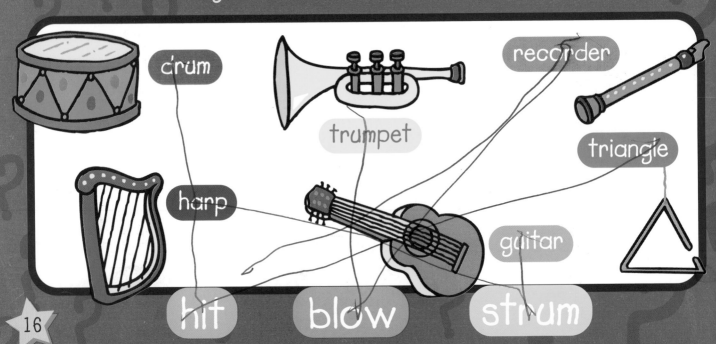

drum
trumpet
recorder
triangle
harp
guitar

hit     blow     strum

# Join up the dots to see some instruments.

These animals want to play instruments which begin with the same letter as their names – can you match them up?

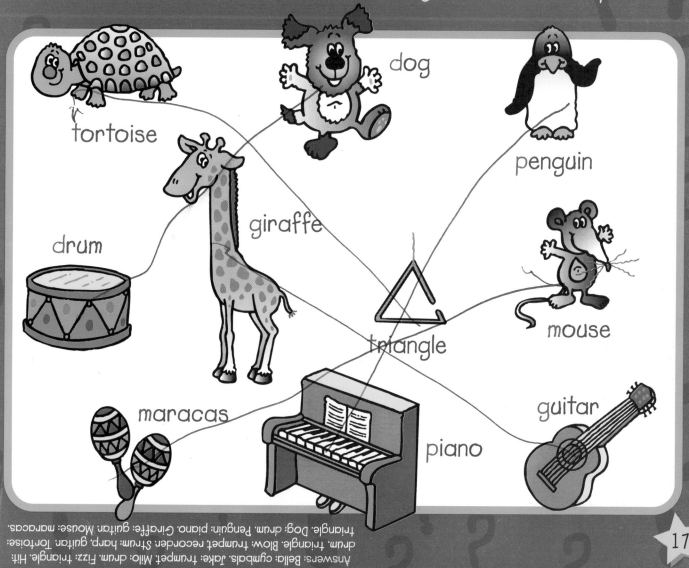

tortoise

dog

penguin

giraffe

drum

mouse

triangle

maracas

piano

guitar

# Let's make music!

You will need: ★ 2 large yoghurt pots ★ paints ★ a paintbrush ★ coloured paper or stickers ★ safety scissors ★ safe glue

## 1 To make a drum...

Paint the yoghurt pots with brightly coloured paint. Leave on the lids – these are what you will bang!

## 2

Cut some spots and stars from coloured paper (or use stickers) to decorate your drums.

18

# 1 To make a trumpet...

Roll a cone shape from coloured paper and decorate it with stickers. Blow through it and say, TOOT!

Now you are ready to play your musical instruments!

TOOT!

BANG! BANG!

# What's the weather?

SUMMER

The bees are buzzing busily
The sun is in the sky
I even saw a butterfly
Flutter by my eye!

WINTER

It's crunchy and it's really white
I love it when it snows
Although it makes me really cold
And gives me chilly toes!

20

There are four seasons every year – winter, spring, summer and autumn.
Can you guess which season it is in each of these pictures?
Write the seasons on the lines! Which season is it now?

AUTUMN

I'd like to hold on to a leaf
As it goes floating by
The wind would blow us really high
Into the misty sky!

Whenever I see puddles
I jump in with a crash
Then jump again – splish splosh splish splosh
And finish with a SPLASH!

spring

# Milo's football game

You will need: ⚽ a large piece of card ⚽ green sticky felt or green paint ⚽ two small cardboard boxes ⚽ white paper ⚽ coloured card ⚽ safety scissors ⚽ glue ⚽ a ping-pong ball

**1**

Cover a large piece of card with green sticky felt or paint it green.

**2**

Cut out some strips of white paper and glue them onto the pitch to make the markings, or use white paint.

**3**

Use two small cardboard boxes to make the goals and cover them in white paper. Stand one at each end of the pitch.

**4**

Roll two pieces of coloured paper to make the blowers. Now all you need is a ping-pong ball and your blow football game is ready! Kick off!

# Mad about Milo...

How much do you know about Milo?
See if you can answer these questions.
Circle the right answers!

1. What would Milo like to be when he grows up?
   A clown   A doctor   A pilot

2. What is Milo's favourite colour?
   Red   Yellow   Blue   Green

3. What is Milo's favourite word?
   Fabarooney   Great   Brilliant

4. What is Milo's favourite toy?
   Toy car   Teddy   Fairy wand

5. Who is Milo's 'best mate'?
   Max   Jake   Doodles   Judy

Answers: 1.A clown 2.Blue 3.Fabarooney 4.Toy car 5.Jake

23

# Spoon Tweenies!

**Messy Time**

You will need: ☐ wooden spoons ☐ material or felt ☐ an elastic band or piece of ribbon ☐ wool ☐ black card ☐ a yellow feather ☐ beads ☐ cotton wool ☐ round-ended scissors ☐ paintbrush ☐ paints ☐ safe glue

**1** Paint the back of a wooden spoon.

**2** Wrap a piece of material around the stick of the spoon and fasten it with an elastic band or a piece of ribbon.

**3** Cut some strips of wool and glue them to the back of the spoon for Bella, Fizz and Judy's hair. Cut pieces of black card for Milo's hair. Stick on some cotton wool for Max's and a bright yellow feather for Jake's!

4

Paint on a mouth and stick on some eyes. Cut out some coloured card for ears and stick them to the side of the spoon. Finally, decorate your Tweenies' clothes and they are ready to play!

wool

felt circles

flowers

beads

Fizz

Milo

Judy

Jake

Bella

Max

25

# Pirates!

Bella wanted to surprise the others by dressing up. So she hid behind the curtain, while she tried on her outfit. "Hurry up, Bella," shouted Jake to the curtain.

"Nearly ready!" cried Bella. "Just need my skull and crossbones." She jumped out from behind the curtain, "Ahoy there, me hearties!" She was dressed in a pirate's hat and a big hairy beard. She had an eye patch on, as she waved a plastic cutlass in the air.

"Do you like my beard, Milo?" asked Bella.

"Err, it's okay," said Milo, "but I prefer the cutlass."

"I want to be a pirate, too!" decided Fizz.

"Yes, me too," said Jake, "I want a gull and crossroads, like Bella."

"That's a skull and crossbones, mate," corrected Milo.

Judy came over to see what they were doing. "Judy, how do we become pirates like Bella?" asked Fizz.

"Well, let's see... we could find some pirate costumes like Bella's for you to wear, and I could draw a map for you to use to hunt for treasure!"

So, they made some eye patches from black paper and elastic, they put hankies on their heads and moustaches under their noses.

Soon they were all ready for their pirate adventure!
Even Doodles joined in.

"It's One-Eyed Doodles!" said Milo, after they'd carefully placed an eye patch on him.

"I'm Captain Beardie Bella!" said Bella. "I'm Fizz the Fright!" said Fizz. "I'll be Muncho Milo," said Milo. "And I'm Jolly Roger Jakey," shouted Jake.

"Now, see if you can find the HIDDEN TREASURE!" said Judy, handing them a map.

"Let's pretend that we're on a big pirate ship, sailing the Seven Seas searching for the treasure!" said Captain Beardie Bella, taking the map. So they sailed far and wide on their big pirate ship! It had ropes and cannons and a crow's nest for seeing far out to sea.

"Pirates make people walk the plank!" cried Milo. So One-Eyed Doodles slowly plodded onto the wooden plank as the Tweenies pretended to make him walk the plank. "AHAR!" cried Bella, as she waved her cutlass at him!

The Tweenie pirates sailed the Seven Seas in search of treasure and new land. Then they remembered the map that Judy had given them. "Right, well it starts here at the purple spot and there's a line to follow," said Muncho Milo.

So they followed the line all the way back to the slide in the garden! One-Eyed Doodles was there, guarding the sandpit.

"Ooh, look, there's an 'X' in the sandpit," said Fizz the Fright.

"We sail around the Seven Seas,
We only need a little breeze,
The only thing that's in our hold,
Is lots and lots of lovely gold!"

"'X' marks the spot," said Jolly Roger Jakey.
"Aha, start digging me hearties," cried
Captain Beardie Bella, handing out spades
to everyone. They all started to dig.
  "I've found the treasure," shouted
Muncho Milo. Then he looked disappointed.
"Oh, it's only One-Eyed Doodles' bone!"
  "Here's the treasure!" said Judy, behind
them. They all turned round and there was Judy
holding a treasure chest full of tasty party goodies - in fact -
it was a REAL pirate's feast!

29

Based on the story written by Iain Lauchlan.

# Make the Jolly Roger!

You will need: ☐ a cereal packet ☐ 3 small cereal packets ☐ a pencil or stick ☐ paints ☐ a paintbrush ☐ paper ☐ safety scissors ☐ safe glue

**1** Cut out the shape of your pirate ship from a cereal packet and stick three small cereal packets inside to make the deck.

**2** Your ship is ready to be painted.

**3**

Cut out some pieces of white paper and glue them to a stick or a pencil to make the mast. Fix it to your ship and you are ready to set sail!

**4**

Don't forget to add a skull and crossbones flag!

'Ahoy there me' hearties!'

"The big ship sails on the Alley, Alley O!"

# Fizz's favourites

My favourite things are ballet dancing, eating pasta, looking at rainbows and going to the seaside. I love dressing up, too – I've been a princess, a fairy, Snow White and even a mermaid!

Look at the pictures below and circle the four things that Fizz likes.

Fizz loves rainbows because they are so colourful. Look carefully at the rainbows below and see if you can spot the odd one out.

1
2
3
4

Do you know what Fizz's favourite colour is?
Which of the following words does it rhyme with?

mellow

kite

shoe

bed

sink

screen

Which colours rhyme with the other words?

# Fizz's fairy cakes!

To make these pretty pink fairy cakes, you will need:
☐ plain cup cakes ☐ pink butter icing ☐ edible silver balls
☐ hundreds and thousands ☐ icing sugar

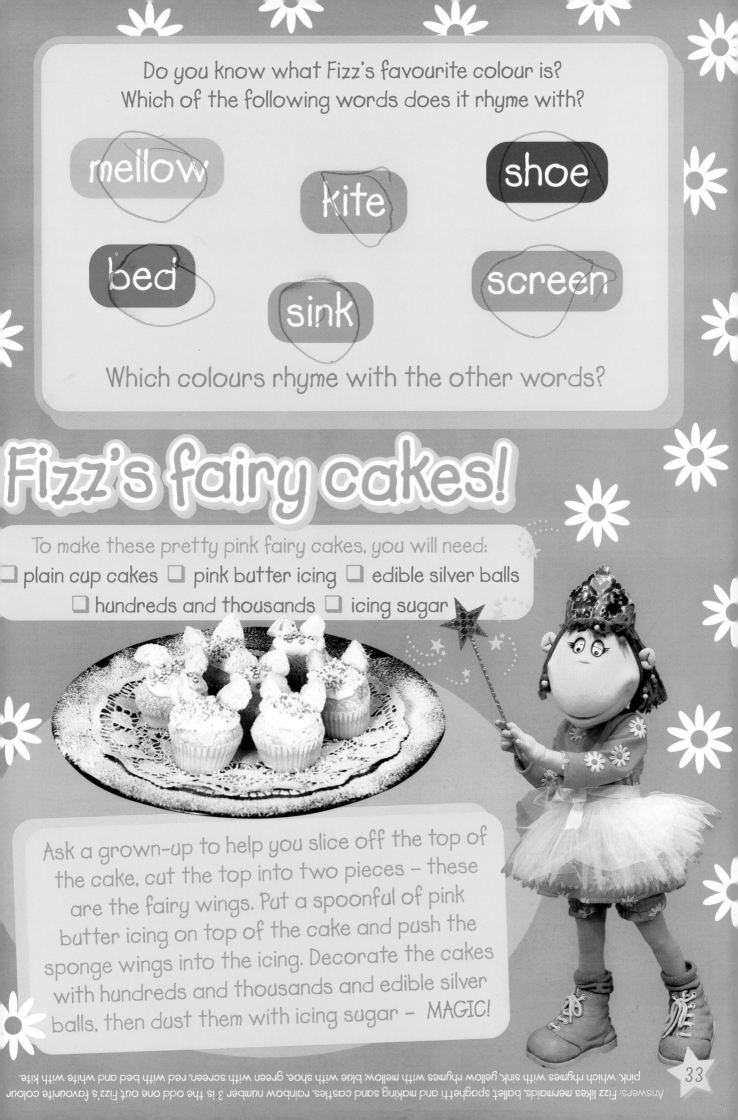

Ask a grown-up to help you slice off the top of the cake, cut the top into two pieces – these are the fairy wings. Put a spoonful of pink butter icing on top of the cake and push the sponge wings into the icing. Decorate the cakes with hundreds and thousands Fizz and edible silver balls, then dust them with icing sugar – MAGIC!

# Amazing animals

The Tweenies wanted to find out about some animals that live in different parts of the world. Here's what they found out...

This gorilla has hands, feet and a face that look a bit like ours. Gorillas live in families just like us too!

What are you looking at?

Blue is *definitely* my colour!

A chameleon is a big lizard which can change colour to hide itself in the wild. This chameleon has changed colour to match the tree that it's perched on!

An anteater has a long snout. This helps it to smell and find ants and other insects to eat. Wave your arm in front of your nose like an anteater!

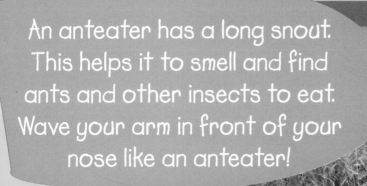

It's lunchtime!

Who's the tallest?

Giraffes have very long necks which help them to reach their food – the leaves from the tops of trees. Can you think of any other animals or birds with long necks?

Doodles is an amazing animal too! That's why we love him. Do you know any amazing animals?

35

# Sssspiral snakes!

**Messy Time**

You will need: ● coloured card ● safety scissors ● paints or sticky shapes ● glue ● thin elastic

Cut out a spiral shape like this one from a circle of coloured card.

Decorate your snake with sticky shapes or paint some patterns on it. Aleena is making a ssstripy snake!

Stick on some eyes and a forked tongue and attach a piece of elastic to the tail.

Sssss

Sssss

Sssss

37

# Jungle search

How quickly can you find the Tweenies in this picture?

38

There are lots of creatures hiding in this jungle. Look at the list at the side of the page – can you find them all?

39

Tick the boxes when you find them!

gorilla

giraffe

tiger

zebra

lion

hippo

elephant

# Oodles of Doodles!

I love to eat my doggy food, drink lots of water and sleep, hmmmm, I love to sleep, all snuggled up on my beanbag... Zzzzzzzzzz.

I love bones which I bury in places where no one will find them – in fact I've hidden four bones, like this one, in your Annual – can you find them all?

(Answer at the bottom of the opposite page!)

I really like my Tweenie friends, they always play with me and take me for walks, sometimes they even clear up my toys if I'm being a bit lazy!

Can you draw lines to match these things to the words to show when I would need them?

hungry    sleepy
messy    walkies!

Write over the dotty letters!

I get up to all sorts of things, like holidays in Eastbone, I chat to my friends on the telebone, I have my hair done at the doggy salon, I get invited to all sorts of groovy parties where we eat hot dogs and ice cream bones!

# Make Doodles!

**1**

Here's what my Doodles is made of...

stock-cube box head

egg box lid body

kitchen roll legs

**2**

Paint the boxes and tubes yellow and red to look like Doodles' fur – you could use felt if you have some.

**3**

Stick all the pieces together and Doodles is almost ready. Don't forget the eyes, ears and nose. Rebecca used felt, but you could use paper or fabric.

The bones are hidden on pages: 20,31,34,51.

Write over the dotty numbers and sing along with us!

6 7 8 9 10

Why did you let it go?
Because it bit my finger so.

Which finger did it bite?
This little finger on my right!

Colour the fish to match their twins in the other pond!

# Dexter's day out

Saturday was a very special day for the Brown family. They were off on a trip to the seaside.

"Let's make an early start," said Mr Brown. Dexter, their pet dog, spun around in excitement.

"Just imagine all the fun I could have at the seaside, splashing in the sea and playing in the sand," he thought to himself.

It was a tight squeeze in Mr Brown's car. There were buckets and spades, deck chairs, beach balls and a picnic – as well as Grandma and Grandpa!

But as the Browns trundled off into the distance, nobody noticed that Dexter had been left behind on the doorstep.

"Woof!" yelped Dexter, sadly. What was he going to do?

He wandered off down the road, dragging his tail behind him... until he heard something.

His ears pricked up at the sound of dogs happily barking and playing.

Dexter stood up on his back legs to look over the fence. On the other side were more dogs than Dexter had ever seen before. There were big ones, little ones, fat ones, thin ones, curly-haired ones, sausage-shaped ones... In fact, every type of dog you could imagine!

Some were splashing around in a swimming pool, while others sat in deck chairs sipping fizzy drinks.

"What fun I could have here," thought Dexter, and squeezed himself through a gap in the fence.

Within seconds, he had leapt onto the diving board, bounced twice and dazzled all the other dogs with a double back-flip and two triple somersaults! Everyone wanted to be Dexter's friend after that.

"Let's go down to see Mr Wilson the butcher," cried Dexter, later. "He's got the juiciest bones in town!"

And before long, they were being served with the biggest, most scrumptious bones Dexter had ever seen.

"What a treat!" thought Dexter, munching away.

When they were all full up, Peter the Poodle suggested that they all bury their bones.

"I can bury mine deeper than you lot!" cried a spaniel, scrabbling in the dirt.

"Watch out for that football!" shrieked a labrador, as a bright ball bounced past them. "Let's chase it!" woofed Dexter, and they all hared off after it.

The dogs were having the time of their lives as they chased the ball towards home.

Meanwhile, the Brown family had arrived back from their trip to the seaside early.

They were very worried about poor Dexter who they had left behind. The children sniffed and snivelled as they thought about how sad and lonely Dexter must have been.

Imagine their surprise when a ball came bouncing down the road chased by Dexter and his new friends.

CRASH! The Browns were knocked to the floor! Dexter was so pleased to see them he gave them all a great big lick!

Mr Brown could hardly believe his eyes when he saw the smile on Dexter's face.

"Dexter! Are you alright?" he cried.

"We've been so worried about you!" said Mrs Brown.

Dexter wagged his tail and woofed as loudly as he could, then he ran into the house followed by his new four-legged friends.

The Browns followed them inside and set the table for all of them... jelly and ice cream was the least they could do for Dexter after leaving him behind!

Over the scrummy food, the Browns listened with envy as Dexter told them everything about his day out. What a wonderful day it had been after all!

# Jake's day

What a busy day Jake has had! Here is a list of all the things he has done today. Can you draw in the hands on the blank clocks to show what time it was? What did YOU do today?

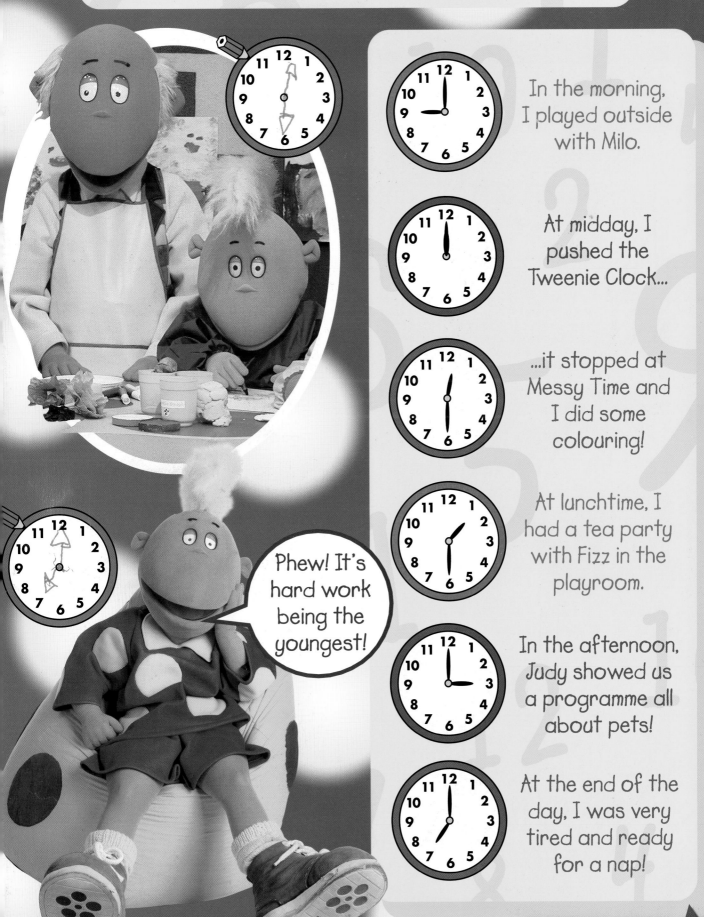

In the morning, I played outside with Milo.

At midday, I pushed the Tweenie Clock...

...it stopped at Messy Time and I did some colouring!

At lunchtime, I had a tea party with Fizz in the playroom.

In the afternoon, Judy showed us a programme all about pets!

At the end of the day, I was very tired and ready for a nap!

Phew! It's hard work being the youngest!

It's dressing up time with the Tweenies!
Make this picture bright and colourful using your crayons or pens.
Which hat would YOU like to wear?

# Three currant buns

Three currant buns in a baker's shop,
Big and round with a cherry on top.
Along came Milo, with a penny one day,
Bought a currant bun and took it away!

Two currant buns in a baker's shop,
Big and round with a cherry on top.
Along came Bella, with a penny one day,
Bought a currant bun and took it away!

One currant bun in a baker's shop,
Big and round with a cherry on top.
Along came Judy, with a penny one day,
Bought a currant bun and took it away!

Here are some ideas for other verses!

Can you find the currant buns in this baker's shop? What else can you see?

Three tasty loaves in a baker's shop,
Big and round with a pattern on top.
Along came Bella, with a penny one day,
Bought a tasty loaf and took it away!

Three birthday cakes in a baker's shop,
Big and round with candles on top.
Along came Fizz, with a penny one day,
Bought a birthday cake and took it away!

We Bake it !

Fresh Cakes

Hot Pies

OPEN

53

# All about Bella

I really like dressing up, especially as a fairy – with wings and a wand! If I was a fairy I would grant you three wishes – what would your three wishes be?

My favourite fairy tale is Little Red Riding Hood – I love acting it out! Do you know the story?

My, what big teeth you have, Granny!

I'm very good at hand clapping games! Do you know any clapping games or songs?

My favourite song is 'You know you have a friend!'
My favourite colour is red.
My favourite food is tomato soup, brown bread, strawberries and ice cream!

I love to bake, especially with my Gran. Here are some Tweenie treats that I baked. Why don't you make some? All you need is some round biscuits, icing and coloured sweeties!

# The great bone hunt!

StoryTime

Whenever you see a picture in this story,
say the word out loud.

 wasn't happy – he'd lost his squeaky  .

"Doggone it!" he said.  looked worried. "  has lost

his favourite toy," she told the others. "Oh dear," said  ,

"we'll help you look for it, Doodles !" So Jake and

joined them in the search for the squeaky  . Milo

looked under Doodles'  . "It's not here," he called

to the others. "It might be outside," said  , as she went

into the garden to look under the slide, but it wasn't there.

 looked behind the  . "It's not here either!" she

The words made into pictures are:

Doodles

bone

Fizz

Bella

Milo

beanbag

56

said. "Maybe the computer will tell us where Doodles' bone is," said  . "Don't be silly, Jakey, the computer won't be able to help!" cried . But as Jake sat down at the – 'SQUEAK!'. He'd sat on Max's ! "Oh, Max's cap made a noise, just like ' bone," giggled Jake. "Wait a minute, Jakey," said Milo, lifting up Max's cap to find the squeaky underneath! "Well done, , you found the bone!" laughed Milo. was happy again, "Squeak, thank you, squeak!" he said, as he grabbed the .

Just then, came over. "Well done, everyone!" he said. "Here are some to say thank you from Doodles!"

Tweenie Clock

Jake   computer   cap   Max   cakes

57

# News Time!

We've done lots of things in our Annual! How much can you remember?

Can you remember the words to 'Three currant buns'? Try and sing it again!

What is Bella's favourite fairy tale?

LiTTLE ReD RiDiNG HOOD

What was the name of Fizz's stripy dinosaur friend?

SuSan

Which season was Jake describing in "What's the weather?"

*Winter*

What is Milo's favourite colour?

*blue*

Can you remember what Doodles does in his spare time?

*burying bones*

# Magic carpet ride!

The Tweenies have whooshed away on a mystical magic carpet ride. Come on the ride with a friend by taking it in turns to throw a dice and move around the board. The first one to reach the Sultan's gold is the winner!

1

**Start**

2

3

4

Hitch a ride with the genie on his cloud – move forward to number 8!

5

6

7

8

9

Look at the view below! Miss a turn while you take a picture!

10

11